Beyond the Walls

New Writing from York St John University

—

2022

LENDAL PRESS

First published in 2022 by Lendal Press
Woodend, The Crescent, Scarborough, YO11 2PW
an imprint of Valley Press · lendalpress.com

ISBN 978-1-912436-85-9
Catalogue no. LP0012

A CIP record is available from the British Library.

Cover artwork, design and other illustrations by Jacob Currie
Text design by Peter Barnfather

Printed and bound in Great Britain by
Imprint Digital, Upton Pyne, Exeter

Contents

YORK ST JOHN COMPETITION WINNERS

Foreword

I'm sat in my living room ruminating on the theme of this year's *Beyond the Walls* anthology, fingers hovering over a keyboard and a blank screen staring back at me. It seems that trying to find a pithy way to start this introduction is trickier than I thought. I had to stop briefly to make an MS Teams call, a form of communication with which we have become all too familiar. I was struck with how easily this piece of technology has become integrated into our lives and how invaluable it has proven itself in many ways. The team who put this anthology together decided on *distance* as this year's theme and a very timely concept it is. We perhaps think of distance as something physical, a gap between us, a negative that has to be endured. This is something that has, in recent years, been challenged. Despite physical distance being thrust upon us we have found increasingly inventive ways to connect and hopefully this has led to a clearer understanding of each other. One of the things you will find in these pages are a range of differing interpretations of distance.

As a verb distance can, of course, mean to separate yourself from something. Through the writing contained herein you will find stories and poems which distance us from difference, from fear and from separation.

As a noun distance is the length between two points and in many ways this describes the writing process. For the writer the distance travelled is from conception, through writing a first draft, redrafting and perfecting their work. However, the final point in the journey is when this is met by you, the reader. In reading this work you are meeting someone else; literature gives us an insight into other viewpoints, other ways of living, different ideas – it allows us to connect with other people, across physical distance, culture and even time.

We live in 'interesting times' and, at the moment the world seeks to lurch from one crisis to the next. There are worries about war, the environment and political extremism. However, as Erich Fromm said, 'Creativity requires the courage to let go of certainties.' Writers work with these uncertainties, giving us a way of negotiating the world. They provide imagined spaces in which we can play out scenarios for living. Spaces where we can become other people and through this to understand them.

Each year we publish a selection of writing from those who study and write in the York Centre for Writing. I have been consistently stunned by the quality and range of writing and this 2022 edition continues that proud tradition. Under the leadership of module director Dr Rob O'Connor and in collaboration with Lendal Press, an imprint of long-established collaborators Valley Press, the students of the Working with Words module on our Creative Writing degree programme have produced a magnificent volume of prose and poetry. This is no easy task. The publishing team have shown tremendous skill, thoughtfulness, and resilience in their work.

It is now time to stop reading this introduction and to delve deeper into the work herein. You will find words to inspire, to reassure, to challenge and to entertain. The work ranges from the deeply personal introspection of 'Imperfect Timing' to the folklore infused 'The Girl and the Dime.' The work in this anthology is resonant and powerful. As Toni Morrison said, 'A writer's life and work are not a gift to mankind; they are its necessity.'

Dr. Robert Edgar, March 2022
Associate Professor of Creative Writing
York St John University

(The anthology team asked me not to directly refer to Covid as this anthology is about so much more. So even though I allude to it above I haven't mentioned it directly. Until now that is.)

Preface

'*Writing a novel is like driving a car at night.*
You can see only as far as your headlights,
but you can make the whole trip that way.'
 – E. L. Doctorow

In the modern world we experience more distance than we have ever known. With technology, we are able to understand the great vastness that is between us. At the same time, we find ourselves so much closer than before. It has become near impossible to distance ourselves from world changing events or from a person across the street. With this being the tenth annual *Beyond the Walls* anthology, we look towards the space between time. As we move further into the future, we are reminded of the memories that we leave behind. Just walking the streets of York shows this expanse: between the founding military fortress to the present live and bustling city. Such distance is rooted at the forefront of our minds at York St John University. While we reach for those in far off lands, we hold close the ones we meet face to face. As we learn from the past, we prepare for the future. With the talent of York St John's creative minds, brought to life by Lendal Press, this anthology is a means to reflect on all kinds of distance.

When you are *Going the Distance*, you truly go *Beyond the Walls*.

Student Editorial Team

Light Years Measure Distance, not Time

Josh Brittain

I didn't feel like me at the weekend. Especially Sunday, with the clocks going forward, dragging me towards a time I didn't want to be a part of. How can time run out? It stretches beyond our comprehension, but Sunday felt one step ahead of me. Like one of those dreams where you can't catch up to whatever you are chasing.

What didn't help was trying to think of something to write for this anthology. I felt pressure. Not pressure to write anything objectively good or industry changing. Just to write anything. Letters, words, sentences that stretch into something at least meaningful, and featuring that vital trait for me, authenticity.

Maybe I was just uninspired. I'm not usually a big fan of writing prompts, I let the ideas come to me. Christ, that was pretentious. But, it's true. I observe, I reflect, and ideas arrive. From where, I couldn't tell you. That's just how it works. Maybe it was brain fog. And every worrying thought that comes with it. Early-set dementia. *Stop looking at your phone, it's destroying your brain.*

My dad just turned seventy and he didn't want to celebrate. He's always been unenthusiastic about birthdays. He hasn't changed much over the last twenty years. He's been bald for as long as I can remember, his moustache has been white forever, and his eyes have always had that piercing icy blue which I have inherited. Thanks Dad. Three years ago, he had his knee replaced. His gait, which had always been a little lopsided from nearly forty years of plastering and building work, seemed to get worse. It didn't help that he fell on it. The stairs in the house became a mountain and he invariably got up in the middle of the night to sleep, sat up, in the rocking chair in the kitchen. In his first fight with Joe Frazier,

Muhammad Ali famously told his legs to move, seconds later he was knocked down by Frazier's legendary left hook. That was Ali's second fight after four years away from the ring. Time takes its toll.

Taylor Hawkins, the drummer for the Foo Fighters, died a few days ago at age fifty. Whatever the circumstances, that is no age to die. Weeks before that, another giant of nineties and noughties music, Mark Lanegan, passed away at fifty-seven. Plenty of years ahead of him. Lanegan had recorded music up until the winter of last year. Hawkins had played a three hour long set a week before his untimely death.

My partner says that 'we're old.' I correct her: 'we're older' or sometimes, 'we're still young.' We still have years, decades even, left. The focus of the world is mostly on people younger than us. The football player, Gavi, made his debut for Barcelona's men's team at sixteen and is now integrated in the first team. Billie Eilish has sold millions and millions of albums, and she's just won an Oscar at twenty. The number isn't important, them being younger than us is what affects my thirty-year-old girlfriend.

It's strange that two people with forty years between them have similar attitudes. I disagree with my girlfriend and my dad. We all get old, but that doesn't mean we stop being young. Rowling didn't get *Philosopher's Stone* published until she was in her thirties, Kevin Nash, a hall of fame professional wrestler, didn't make his debut until he was thirty-two. But I'm not far away. I look at my peers at university, some of which are nearly twelve years younger than me and my growing disdain for social media. I'm not light years away.

I started playing eleven-a-side football again just before the lockdown kicked in. Although the season was interrupted, that wasn't the worst thing. I felt a pain in my ass. A literal one. It turned out to be a condition known as Piriformis syndrome (it's the muscle that connects the bottom of your spine to the top of your thighs). I couldn't sprint, I could kind of run, walking up and down stairs became difficult. I didn't have an artificial limb, but it felt like it. I have always been quick, now it felt like my legs couldn't get going, like my legs weren't mine.

Distance and time are irrevocably linked. We measure them in relation to the other, *miles* per *hour*. Google maps tells us how far away our destination is and how long the journey will take. One light year is approximately six trillion miles. An incomprehensible amount. We don't suddenly become old when we reach a defined age. Our bodies grow old, our hair turns grey, but mentally, we are as young as we tell ourselves.

The Girl and the Dime

Yulka Banaszek

There has always been a need for me to let myself be devoured by the woods. It wasn't that simple, of course. The woods expect respect from you. That's what I gave it when I ran away from the village. The fae guided me well, ever since I was born. What would I have done without them? My beloved.

I dug my hands into the dirt, trying to find the golden coin that I had found the day before. Villagers had a careless nature. They couldn't hold sacred what was outside their houses and neither what was inside them. That is why I left. That is why I never wanted to go back. My fingers touched the cold metal and pulled it from under the leaves. It glistened in the morning sun, a faded face stencilled on one side, an eagle on the other. I remember how many of them I used to carry around in the pockets of my dress; how many of them I used to spend. Giving the gold away for sweet treats would only satisfy me for a moment before leaving me craving again.

My head shot up when I heard the gentle sound of bells in the distance. I jumped, letting the coin fall onto the ground again, I hid behind a tree big enough to cover my frame. The fae always warned me of danger – they warned me of the villagers.

There has never been a villager on the road this early. I heard a horse approaching and held my breath when it stopped. Then came a heavy thud on the ground and the rustling of leaves. I shut my eyes; hands clenched. The steps stopped on the other side of the tree only to disappear into the distance again.

I took a deep breath and lurked around the tree. The villager was gone, and so was the coin. I shouldn't have mourned soulless material. I shouldn't have let it enter my mind and make my heart feel heavy. What would I have done with it anyway? I never went to the market, though sometimes I watched from the edge as most of the villagers rarely passed by the woods. They feared what may wander amongst the trees, especially at night. I was glad about it. The trees hated them. I could hear them whispering to each other when their branches shook, and their leaves rustled in the breeze.

The coin didn't leave my mind. My thoughts circled around the golden object and each time I tried to let it go I felt my eyes moving to the spot I last saw it. It was my prized possession, something that was new and different to my collection. I wanted it back – the forest wanted it back. But where was I supposed to look for it? The leaves didn't hide it, the man must have taken it. The man with the blue coat. The fae told me. I saw him frequently riding through the trees, sometimes taking shortcuts, nearly passing my hut.

I rummaged through wooden bowls and buckets I had carved myself, to find berries I collected the day before. As I was about to eat, I heard the bells again. The fae formed a glistening line towards the village in the distance. I shook my head, but the wind gave me a push from the back.

My feet carried me closer to the edge of the forest. Today the traveling market was in town. Merchant after merchant lined up at the marketplace, selling everything from fish to jewellery. Something blue caught my eye. The man. With a smile spread across his face, he marched through the crowd of people, greeting everyone along his way. He stopped to help an elderly merchant load his wagon with sacks of corn and waited until he took off before putting his hands on his hips.

Our eyes met for the first time and my body froze. His smile changed into a frown, and he began to move towards me. I took a few steps back, not able to look away from him. Then, before I was able to run deeper into the woods, he caught up with me.

'Hello,' his voice was soft.

I looked up at him.

'I have seen you before.'

I didn't believe him. No one could see me. Not when I didn't want them to.

'Impossible.'

'You surely are like a cat in the dark,' he said, a smile dancing on his lips.

'I have to go.'

And then I ran. He yelled after me. I didn't stop. I hid inside my hut, hoping he wouldn't find me. Hoping he didn't run after me; hoping he'd forgotten me. I knew it was too late.

On the second day, I walked back, only for him to find me again. This time we talked. He told me his name, his age, his favourite dance. He told me about his dying grandma, his love for singing, the day he had lost his first horse.

On the third day, he took my hand and guided me to a tailor where he purchased a loose pink dress for me.

On the fourth day, he kissed me.

On the fifth day, he brought me a lily.

On the sixth day, the lily wilted.

On the seventh day, he wasn't waiting for me.

On the eighth day, I saw him kissing another girl.

I watched them hold hands as they talked to each other with the sun in their faces. She was beautiful, so was he. He didn't look my way. He wasn't looking for me. I wondered if he had forgotten about me; if he thought I had been a blurry dream.

The universe has a plan for each and every one of us. We only receive what we are meant to receive. I decided to never visit the village again. It has brought me pain once, then twice.

Three days later, I saw both of them riding through the woods, her laughter ringing in my ears. As they passed, I heard a familiar noise. My head peered around the tree, seeing something shimmering on the ground between branches and cobwebs. The stencil on the dime caught my eye as I kneeled, picking up what I had once lost. I put the golden coin into my bag and watched him ride away with his lover while I disappeared behind the branches.

I was never yours.

You were never mine.

At Broken Scar *

Stephen Bishop

North-tied, I watch the rock-strewn Tees stream past
My lazy Southern rivers did not flow so fast;
They sprang warm, not rushing cold over rocky shards
Their banks spring green-leafed, reaching sunwards.

Twenty years of North have I now endured
But still to this place I am not inured;
Away from the golden places I knew
Away from towns I could not return to.

But soon my child is eighteen, set to fly
And I need no longer simply stand by;
Dare I now go back there, go back home?
Dare to go Southwards again, cease to roam?

The love that brought me Northwards burned so bright,
And I went without a doubt.
I dared then,
I want to dare again.

* A beauty spot on the River Tees near Darlington, popular
with families

Devon's Ghost

Kes Bonnage

The car rolled to a stop outside of the old, worn farmhouse. It stood alone down a beaten track off the A171 between Ravenscar and Robin Hood's Bay, far out on the moorland. The heavy rain that had pelted the windshield the entire drive cascaded down its sad stone façade, as though it was weeping.

'Is this it, Mama?' asked Devon, in a vain attempt to see the house from his booster seat.

Cara knew that Devon was anxious about the move. The long car journey here from Manchester certainly hadn't helped with the little boy's nerves, and she wanted to avoid a meltdown before they had at least gotten into their new home.

'Yes, baby. We're going to live here now. It's exciting, isn't it?' Cara said, injecting her voice with as much false cheer as she could, 'We'll have so much space to run and play, and you can be as loud as you want when Mama isn't working.'

'I don't have to be quiet for neighbours?'

'Nope.'

'Wow,' Devon whispered as he clutched his beloved stuffed dinosaur to his chest. Cara could already hear all the roaring he was sure to 'practise' – he had the space now, so why wouldn't he?

The move-in was uneventful, thankfully, if a little wet. Cara hadn't brought much with her from Manchester, mostly things for Devon: toys, stuffed animals, his favourite blanket, and a few picture books. Cara got him settled in the room next to hers before putting away the food she bought in Fylingdales, the nearest town.

Later that evening, as she climbed the stairs to grab Devon for dinner, Cara paused on the landing.

'And this is my brontosaurus, Brunnie – did you know that brontosaurus' were even bigger than elephants! …Don't be silly, of course she won't grow to be bigger than an elephant! Brunnie is a baby brontosaurus…'

Devon was talking to someone. Cara rushed across the landing.

'Who are you talking to, baby?'

Devon looked up at Cara as if she were stupid.

'Mrs. Hall.'

'Mrs. Hall?'

'Yeah, she's right there, Mama. Can't you see her?' Devon pointed to a vacant corner of the room.

Cara took a breath and ruffled Devon's hair. At six years old, Devon was a little old to be developing imaginary friends, but Cara supposed the stress of the move and the divorce had caused him to regress a little.

'Oh, hello Mrs. Hall. Sorry for my earlier rudeness,' Cara said, addressing the empty corner, 'but this little monkey needs to come downstairs and eat his dinner.'

Devon cheered and made to run downstairs – he paused briefly. He marched excitedly to the corner, placing his stuffed dinosaur down there.

'To keep you company when I'm not here…you're welcome!'

Ever since the divorce Cara had been unable to pry that stuffed dinosaur from Devon's grip. It had to be in his sight at all times. The one time she had tried to wash the poor matted thing Devon had screamed and screamed until it was returned, still dirty.

'Are you coming, Mama?' Devon yelled up the stairs. Cara pulled her gaze away from the corner, rubbed her eyes, checked that yes, the stuffed dinosaur was still there, and made her own way downstairs.

'Coming baby!'

* * *

The pair settled into their new lives easily enough. Cara worked from home in the mornings and spent the afternoons doing housework, cooking, and looking after their small flock of chickens. Devon attended the nearby primary school in Fylingdales. Every evening, after school, Devon would rush up to his room and prattle away to the empty corner until Cara called him for dinner. This evening was no different.

'…And then Lucy C grabbed her pencil and—'

'Devon, come on, dinner time,' Cara leaned on the doorframe and beckoned her son forward.

'Oka– uh, Mama, Mrs. Hall says I can't go yet. I have to finish my story.'

There was a brief silence.

'Well, tell Mrs. Hall that you can finish your story after dinner.'

Devon looked at the empty corner.

'She says 'very well', but she's not happy about it.'

Cara eyed the corner suspiciously for a moment before chastising herself for such a silly reaction.

'Come on, little boys need to eat.'

* * *

'Devon, I've had enough of this! You are going to school.' Cara had reached the end of her tether. They were already twenty minutes late as it was.

'No!' Devon cried, pulling at Cara's sleeve and glancing at the corner anxiously, 'Mrs. Hall says I have to stay here, or else she'll hurt Brunnie!'

'I'll be here all day, Devon, and I'll protect Brunnie, I promise. We can even take her in the car with us on our way to school.'

The stuffed dinosaur was perched on the end of the bed. Cara went to grab it, but Devon pulled her back.

'Stop Mama! She's gonna hurt her!'

'How?' Cara asked, exasperated, 'How will missus Hall hurt Brunnie? She's not real!'

Cara grabbed the stuffed dinosaur by its long tail and held it up.

'See, baby, it's fi—'

Brunnie, as if by magic, suddenly caught aflame. Cara shrieked. The flames burnt her fingers. She dropped the dinosaur, and as it fell it turned into nothing more than ash.

Devon clung to Cara's leg, pushed his face into her jeans, and screamed.

* * *

Selling the farmhouse had been a hassle. Cara couldn't answer any questions about why she wanted to move so suddenly.

'Farm life was far harder than I thought.'

'It just wasn't for us.'

'Devon didn't adjust well,' – excuses, excuses.

Cara didn't want to move in with her parents, back in Manchester, back where she'd started, but she had no choice. It would be a squeeze. She and Devon had to share a room, and a bed, but anything was better than the farmhouse. Anything.

Weeks later – after they'd settled – Devon shot awake one night, clutching his new stuffed T-Rex. He fixed his gaze, unblinking, on the foot of the bed. As if compelled to look. It took him a moment to understand what he saw.

'I missed you, Brunnie…'

Between Us

Emma Brimelow

At twelve
I told my mother that I was a lesbian.
When you know you know,
thinking that she would accept me,
open armed, rosy-cheeked.
Unconditional, dessert-making, brownie baking love.
Instead, her knuckles whitened
around a whisk covered in cookie mix
as she stood – silent.

Your tea goes cold on the dining room table
and knives are missing
from the drawer next to
the oven,
now containing nothing but burnt pastry ends
and a stray choc chip.

Tear-stained tea towels
as she explains that
just because you thought your best friend was pretty
Doesn't make you
'One of those homosexuals.'

These words she projected.
She spat them loudly enough to shatter me into
a thousand tiny pieces
and I'm scattered across the kitchen countertops.
Where she could scrape the remnants together
and bake them into a Victoria sponge,
perhaps a tiramisu, or a cheesecake.
Sickly-sweet flavours like her language of love.

A language of love that can only be spoken
     between man and woman.

Whisked egg whites peak into meringue mountains,
resembling breasts.
Can't get the image of girls out of my head
yet as I look closer every one of them is
my mother.

Sour-faced,
disappointment laced.

No, you can't lick the spoon,
not anymore.

As she scrapes raspberry jam out of a glass jar and
smothers it over a shortcrust pastry,
I am reminded that love can never be
unconditional.

Holding on to the Pretence

Emma Cairns

I felt the shifts every morning as I woke; the way the world drifted further away from us. The compassion of humanity crumbled with the burning forests, became submerged by the rising oceans, choked on the pollution in the air.

All we could do was stand and watch.

* * *

2025: salvation

It wasn't always a house wrapped in solitude. Until a year ago it was a third-floor apartment somewhere deep in the city centre. It wasn't always a place that people only visited to escape the fast-life they'd become temporarily bored with.

The exterior of the house was entrancing when the sun drenched it in just the right amount of light; ivy stretched further and further up the whitewashed stone; displays of colourful flowers nestled in the window boxes. Sometimes people realised it was the epitome of their 'décor inspiration' Pinterest boards. Suddenly their interest was piqued.

But most of the time they couldn't seem to escape the patchy internet connection or the almost non-existent phone reception. And none of us could escape the unbearable cold seeping into every crevice, filling the gaps between aching bones.

I never found connections to the city, and it wasn't for the lack of trying. I found a job I didn't hate, spent my lunch breaks outside, became a regular in too many coffee shops. I also spent every waking moment – or what felt like that – thinking about the current state of the world. The guilt still pumps the blood through my veins a little too fast sometimes, dizzying my senses.

I joined climate protests, shouted above the noise of the crowds, created a life I thought was helping me and the planet. It wasn't until I found myself in the middle of the countryside that I realised the contributions I thought I was making were meagre. I'd barely scratched the surface.

From the apartment, I used to see the identical buildings staring at me from across the street. If I pressed my face flat enough to the glass, I could see the congested road below. The sun made its cameo at midday, then dipped behind the tired grey cityscape not long after.

My plants wilted and the rooms grew cold.

The kettle finished boiling with an abrupt *click* and I untangled myself from the past. I spilled hot water over the sides of the mug, a searing pain on my thumb for no more than half a second. I watched the teabag as it was carried to the surface, watched as the milk blended the glassy brown into something rich and flavourful.

I returned to my makeshift desk on the sofa in the living room, my laptop balanced on a tray, my notepad and pen lost between the crumpled blankets and yellow cushions. I gently put my tea on a coaster on the floor and went to my bookshelf tucked away in the corner. A layer of dust had started to collect. My fingers danced over the creases in the spines of the well-read books, over the titles in bold and cursive and calligraphy. Sometimes, when there was nothing else to do, I would rearrange them: alphabetically, colour-coordinated, author names. Nothing worked; they were restless. I seemed to have given them a mind of their own.

I turned on the news. I would rather watch something else, anything else, but the coverage was unusually captivating; far more exciting than anything happening at the house. It was one of the very few glimpses I had into the outside world that I desperately tried to separate myself from.

Wildfires. Earthquakes. Volcanic eruptions. Floods. Tsunamis. State of Emergency. The climate crisis. Conspiracy theory debunked: climate change will not end the world in seven years.

* * *

2026: destruction

When the world burst into flames and erupted into anarchy, it left a layer of ash that blocked out the sun for far too long. I didn't go outside; I didn't see anyone. I settled with the silence of the house.

Most people survived. Then the supplies ran out. The seasons stopped. People changed.

I remember the first month without power. The first night, the house plummeted into an impenetrable darkness. I guided myself to the kitchen, moving my hands along the walls, feeling for the familiar indentations and for the photo frames I'd left in place. I found the light switch, clicked it on and off. Nothing happened.

The kitchen tiles were icy beneath my bare feet. I stood for a moment in an attempt to distinguish the shapes of the room.

The matches and candles were stashed in the top left cupboard above the microwave. *The microwave.* It wouldn't work if there was no power, nor would the oven, the kettle, or the refrigerator. *Of course they wouldn't.* I knew this. I'd planned for it. But only because I never thought I'd have to live through it. I'd assumed that the excessive planning was merely a way to pass my time until the world reverted to its old ways and patterns that I thought I loathed.

I'd give anything to have them back.

I lit the candles I'd taken from the cupboard and carried them back to the living room on a tray, stopping every few paces when the flames became too lively. I looked at the labels: *cherry*, *pomegranate*, *fresh linen*, *strawberry*, *mango*. They were all odourless, of course.

Earth wasn't the same planet I knew. No matter where I went or what I did, I was reminded that it was devoid of the one thing I longed to escape from in the time Before. It was devoid of life.

* * *

2027: rebirth

I hold the locket between my thumb and forefinger and take the crumpled photograph from the pocket of my cardigan. It's been a long time since I looked at it. It stirs a disbelief within me that *this* is what's left. We knew what would happen and we chose not to listen for the fear of not knowing what it would bring. The intensity of regret is harder to live with.

I turn the photograph over, look at the word scrawled in black ink: '*Before*'.

I close my eyes and think about the 2025 calendar still hanging on a rusty nail in the kitchen wall, full of dates that have long since held any importance. I think about the silent sadness dripping down the walls of the house. I think about how close I am to the ocean. The waves impatiently rush against the beach, determined to rise.

I open my eyes and look to where the horizon gently meets the water, the sky alight with deep hues of orange and pink. The first glimpse of a sunset in the aftermath was always going to be the most beautiful; the most entrancing.

Instinctively, I pull the broken disposable camera from my coat pocket, squinting through the impossibly small lens. I know it doesn't work, but I find a comfort in holding on to the pretence that everything is just as normal as it always has been.

Pull

Charlotte Carlile

His glove scraped across the metal as he gripped the next hand-hold, pulling himself further along the spaceship. The metallic scraping was muffled by his helmet. This job was dangerous. It was the only time they had to be outside of the ship and exposed to all of the dangers inherent within that — the cold, oxygen depletion, getting lost or cut off. He always volunteered for it.

He grabbed another hold, feeling his wedding band pressing hard into the metal through his glove. The rope wrapped around his waist tugged again as it unspooled, reassuring him that he was still safe; that he could still find his way back home.

Home.

His throat tightened. He swallowed, and grasped for another handhold, pulling himself further across.

He tried to ignore the tiny blue-green planet that spun inexorably beneath him.

Home.

That was the spaceship now, though his colleagues were merely colleagues beneath their veneer of friendship and teamwork. No one here knew him. No one here wanted to know him. His shoulders felt so light, and his mind so clear. Right now, it was just him and the void. He could float away into it right now and no-one would miss him.

The rope tugged again.

He was there, at the filter that needed to be cleaned. He got straight to work. His colleagues wouldn't let him be if the ship shut down. They wouldn't so much like the idea of rotting slowly in a hollowed-out metal coffin, even if they were already doing so. They just didn't like to think of it that way.

He looked steadfastly at the part as he scrubbed. Not behind, and definitely not below.

And yet, somehow as always, he ended up with it in his view.

Home, a part of him whispered, though he tried to silence it.

And yet, was a home really a home when you had no one left in it who knew you? When it was filled with echoes and ghosts and slow, horrible, creeping silence?

He cleaned far rougher than was really necessary.

It didn't stop the thoughts though.

The bitter sting of tears as his mother slammed the door in his face, spitting insults he couldn't bear to repeat, not even in the safety of his own mind.

The cold biting into his bones as he huddled on freezing concrete in a thin sleeping bag for warmth. He remembers barely sleeping; ever-watching, ever-wary.

The joy of a waiting list finally reaching his name. A warm bed, a duvet. Heating. A safe place to leave his stuff. Then, by some miracle, a job. Then a stable job. Then a man – bright and wonderful, with a gorgeous smile. His family, so welcoming and accepting that they took him in without question and treated him like a son. His father taking him out on fishing trips, his mother who taught him how to cook one day when he confessed he could barely boil water. His sister, though a teenager, never complained about his sudden presence in her life.

But, as always, life came crashing back into his joy right after the wedding. The death of his father-in-law from an unexpected heart attack at forty-nine shattered them both, and they never quite managed to make themselves whole again. His husband grew distant and uncommunicative in response to his need for support, which only made him clingier and his husband more distant. And thus, the cycle repeated.

Walking in on him with another man was barely a surprise when it happened. Just another dull ache in his heart to join the rest.

The divorce barely registered. He threw himself into his career instead, avoiding people at every opportunity. Most got the point and drifted away.

A few people stayed though, and they forced him to stay tethered to society.

To life.

Two sharp tugs on the rope. He realised that his oxygen was running low. The filter was clean – it was time to go. As he grasped the first handhold, he contemplated just...taking too long.

But only for a moment.

And as he stepped back into the ship, Alexis was waiting for him. She looked harassed. Stressed.

'What's wrong?' he asked.

She looked surprised, but answered. 'Just everything to do and no time to do it in.' And a crooked smile crossed her face.

He smiled back tentatively. The space between them felt more finite.

She became more business-like. 'I'll let you go. Your call with... Jennifer? Is soon, right?'

He nodded. 'My mother-in-law. My ex mother-in-law. She stuck by me after...you know. Anyway, thank you.'

She nodded sympathetically.

There was an awkward pause before he nodded clumsily at her and hurried away.

The video link loaded slowly but surely. Jenny's face was already set in a smile as she finally appeared on the screen.

'How was your day?' she asked.

Unwanted Legacy

Sandra Coatham

Was it always there? Dormant, hermetic,
  hidden behind the daily grind
Manifest by something I did, or didn't do
Too busy attending to the bodies and minds of everyone else,
  neglecting the physical, ignoring the forewarning
Teaching me a lesson, to be grateful...
I am grateful

Telling others is harder than knowing
Don't assume that words unsaid are sufficient
That quietness is acceptance
Or understanding
I know.

Cut it out, excise the fear
Burn...it – extinguish the doubt
Starve it out, erase the sustenance
Block...it. Deny...it
I am scared

When judgement rears up, thwart it
A tearful girl on the train – remember the sorrows
  of adolescence – I miss it
She knows and it matters, matters to her
Give compassion and time
I don't judge

Reject bitterness, that does not help
Live in the present, that is all you have
'Don't let yesterday use up too much of today' *
It no longer lives in me…
I get to live

The realisation
The further I move away from this behemoth
The greater its interest in my daughter

* Cherokee proverb 'Don't let yesterday use
  up too much of today.' – Will Rogers
  goodnewsnetwork.org/will-rogers-quote-on-yesterdays

The Ghost of Rookhurst

Lucy Cummings

In the North Yorkshire Dales lies a village called Gayle. There isn't much to mark the tiny hamlet that gets few visitors and even fewer tourists. There is a mill to their name, and that's all. You could say I was exiled there for a while. I can't remember how they worded it, what expressions they had when they declared that I would be sent there. My memory started going fuzzy a year before, and it wasn't until I was abandoned in Gayle that I started to see the sky again and smell the oncoming flowering of spring.

I met a great-aunt I loved as a child, barely remembering her face from an eternity passing by. I had become a different person – with gaps in my memory and a family that said I wasn't fit for purpose with my glitching brain.

I could now grasp the person I had once been in Gayle, and sense how much of a phantom I had become – or I thought I could until he turned up in my room and demanded I leave the property immediately.

He stood firmly. At least, he would have if his feet weren't floating a few inches away from the battered floorboards. The house, Rookhurst, was Georgian, but he had a decidedly Victorian look about him. A spark of shock came to my veins through the numbness that had overtaken me.

'You do not belong here. You are trespassing,' he said through gritted teeth. I continued to blink at him without speaking.

He was rather striking for a ghost, with little greying to his outlines and vividness still holding to his eyes and hair. He was dressed finely, all his clothes crisp. He seemed ready to greet a Victorian tea party.

Yet, incongruous to it all, was a strange mark on the inside of his left wrist, akin to that of an old Norse rune with all its harsh lines.

'My great-aunt owns this house, if anything you are trespassing,' I replied softly, forcing myself to turn away.

When I peered over my shoulder, he had vanished.

It became its own kind of ritual, his strange eyes highlighting my time in Gayle. My nerves would give a suspicious tingle whenever he was near, and then his blurred outlines would come into focus a few feet from me. He always gave me space. I should have wanted it, the dignity and privacy he gave me, but when I settled down on the massive bed occupying the front bedroom of the house and touched the strange raw scar on the side of my head, all I wanted was someone's voice – even that of a ghost who had ordered me to leave.

There was a passion to him that hadn't been in the people who had abandoned me in Gayle, nor in my great-aunt who was frail and often dozed between trips out to sit quietly reading in the back garden. Had I known noise before, would I have craved it now?

On the eighth day, I caught him looking at the shaved side of my head, the scar exposed from under the longer strands I had tied up in a messy knot.

'You can ask,' I said, flipping through the pages of a battered book Muriel assured me I had loved as a child.

'It would not be fair,' he said, crossing his arms and directing his gaze to my book.

'Why?'

'Because then you would be owed a question about me.'

I laughed lightly. 'Would the answer really be so bad?'

I couldn't help but glance at his wrist where the strange mark was inked into his skin. It was not as cleanly done as a tattoo but more like that of a brand, strikingly contrasting his pale skin.

'Muriel said you were brought here because of an accident. You will only stay until you recover. I, however, am cursed to haunt this place forever. We are different creatures, and it would do no good to have our fates tangled together.' His tone was firm, eyes slightly unfocused, like a gnarl of memories were dragging him under.

I blinked at him. 'Muriel talks to you?'

He shrugged. 'She talks to herself. I cannot help it if I overhear.'

I touched the scar, tracing it along the length of my head. 'I remember being driven here, but that's all. I have nothing to tell you, no answers for myself, and no memories of who I am. Just my name, Freya, and this house.'

'You truly remember nothing?' he said, incredulous.

I shook my head. 'Every time I try it makes me panic, and then I wonder if I am better off not knowing. Muriel keeps giving me such pitying looks. I don't want to know why I deserve such a thing. I'd rather you didn't know, either.'

He sniffed at the teapot that sat beside me, expression softening at the scent of Earl Grey. 'It is better for others not to know more about yourself than you do – it is a horrid weakness to have.'

I bit my lip. 'You said you were cursed to stay here, does that mean you can never move on?'

His gaze shot to mine, a hard edge to it, tempered with intrigue. 'If there was a way, would you help me do it?'

A bargain with the devil. The saying came to my head with a voice I couldn't put a name to, the panic gnawing at me because of its foreignness. Part of me was glad he was trapped here as I was – I wasn't alone if he was forced to haunt the house for eternity. Immediately, I felt guilt at drawing comfort from such a horrible circumstance. He seemed like a good enough person to deserve peace.

'Of course,' I said quickly.

A grin came to his lips, and I was taken aback at how alive it made him; a look of delight glittered in his eyes.

'Perhaps it is better our fates have crossed, Freya,' he said, bowing. 'It is a pleasure to make your acquaintance. My name is Alexander.'

'Alexander…?' I trailed off, sure a surname would follow.

He tilted his head, still smiling. 'I think Alexander will do for now. Tell me, how far would you go to save my soul, darling Freya?'

My heartbeat began to hasten, and I revelled in the sensation of life in it.

'Whatever it takes, I suppose.'

Last Date Café

Imogen Davies

I dragged my nails under the table,
Rust collecting beneath,
And your stare stung me like bleach.
You spilled out the words I withheld
From my lips:
Where do we go from this?

The waiter poured us tea
To sip and not taste.
Stammering a fictional excuse, I blushed
And you – you, my love – gave an appropriate reply.
Then disappointment nestled in your eyes
As I gave no tears,
Bade farewell like a doll in your arms.

This head was
Distant—
And I paid for it.
There is no little haven or grove to dip into
As car doors slam
As you, shrinking around the bend,
Blur into trees.

The iron chair screeches against the tiles
As I stand up
Slowly.
I tip with the ring that slips from my finger,
Clink, onto the saucer.
Leave.

Marjorie

Olivia de Marco

'Cigarette?'

I shake my head. She balances the thin, paper stick on her bottom lip and pulls out a lighter. Each click strikes my eardrum, bullet shells hitting the ground.

'Those things'll probably kill you.'

'With any luck.'

I snigger. 'So, you did the whole family thing.'

'You said I should.'

'I said you could.'

She huffs, the smoke hissing between the gaps in her teeth.

'Do you love them?' I ask.

'I don't know.' She takes another drag. 'That's bad, isn't it? I mean, I know plenty of women who don't love their husbands, but I'm supposed to love my kids, right? I pushed them out of me. The last one ripped me open!'

'Stop.' I gesture at covering my ears.

'What about you? The guy you brought along, is he yours?'

I glance over my shoulder, through the window into the house, where Chester is chatting with her husband. 'No, he's from work. He came along for…moral support.'

'He seems like a good guy.'

'Yeah, he is.'

I wait, then. For her to ask the question that has been sitting at the back of her throat, waiting for her gag reflexes to kick in. She retches and it spills over the garden path in front of us.

'The incidents in London, did you know anything about them?'

'Not at first. But it would have been so much worse if I hadn't gotten involved.'

'You got involved?' Her voice rises so quickly that I have to look straight at her for the first time since we came outside. 'Why would you get involved? Why would you get any closer? Why wouldn't you pack up your life and get as far away from that as possible?'

I shrug. 'Apparently, I've grown some kind of conscience since we last saw each other.'

'You fought harder than any of us to get out of that place. But you never really left it behind, did you?'

'And when exactly did you start smoking?'

She looks away, takes another drag, a few ashes falling on her garish floral-print skirt.

'Does it give you any relief,' I nod at her crumbling cigarette, 'or are you just used to the feeling of your fingers burning?'

And the two of us festered in the smoke for a while.

'Is it that obvious?' she murmurs.

'Your room.'

'You went through my things.'

If I wasn't so happy to see her, I'd be insulted that she'd think anything less of me. 'The hospital corners. The manicure set in the bathroom. You organise your books by the Dewey Decimal Classification method, but you keep Horace and Wilfred Owen in the bottom draw of your bedside table. Hidden, but within arm's reach.'

'You haven't changed at all.'

I wonder if she's right. After all the names, the years of Chester trying to make an honest woman out of me. Even after London. Am I still the same person I was at eighteen?

'Did you go after Robbie?'

His name prickles in my chest. 'I told you I wouldn't.'

'Have you seen him since?'

'No.'

'So what *have* you been doing?'

'This and that. Odd jobs. I sometimes do work at Chester's company.'

'And Chester works for…?' she queries, one eyebrow raised.

She could never do that all those years ago; I bet she practised in the mirror.

'The government.'

'Christ.' She brings the back of her hand to her forehead. '*You*... working for the government? What else have you gotten yourself into?'

'I don't work *for* the government. I just...handle certain things for them.'

'Of course, you do. Just like we were taught to.'

'It's not like that.'

'And then the attacks in London—'

'I told you. I had nothing to do with those.'

'What about him?' She jerks her free hand back at the house. 'Does he even know your real name?'

I don't answer. Instead, I pull an identification card from my pocket – one with a face that belongs to her and a name that doesn't – and hold it between my fingers the same way she holds the cigarette. 'And what about this?'

She taps her cigarette over her ashtray, then sighs, the smoke coming through her nose. 'It's for the bad days,' she says, plucking the card from my fingers and tucking it into her fist.

'Hmm. Most women like you just take methamphetamines.'

'Do you know any women like me?'

I laugh, short and harsh, then shake my head. I look over her immaculately kept lawn, trimmed rose bushes, weedless flower-beds. I might keep the handiwork of our childhood underneath the surface, but she lays it out around her, a proud exhibition of the macabre.

'Look at us.' She blows out one final cloud of smoke and places the remaining stub of the cigarette neatly in her ashtray. 'Two animals dressed up as people.'

'How far we've come...from people dressing up as animals.'

She hums, in agreement or concession; I'm not sure which. Picking up her ashtray, she stands. 'I have to start preparing dinner. You and your friend are welcome to stay if you wish.'

'Would you like any help?' I ask, staying seated.

'And knowingly put a knife into your hand? I think not.'

I laugh again, properly this time, and she joins in.

'Come inside. Meet my husband.'

'What's he like?'

'Oh, he's a sweetheart. You'll hate him.'

I listen to her light, regular footfalls as she walks to the door. I hear her pull down the handle and open it, but not so far that it creaks, before muttering, 'Do you ever go back to the house?'

'No,' I lie.

'Me neither.' She lies too.

Out of Myself

Llykaell Dert-Ethrae

Ivy, ever winding
shrouds my moon:
a façade of trees
and drowning shade.

She speaks to me,
twining threads,
stitching the rivers
that break my banks.

Old paths renew
singing their peace:
those familiar roads
I forgot to travel.

New avenues of light:
her trails of fantasy.
All the delicious fruits
poisoning me.

Take it out of my hands.

Take me out of myself.

If I could but cry;
My oceans were stolen
by smiles on high
and naked delights.

If I could but cry;
My shores left behind
I struggle to see
all that I was.

This is what it is
to drown.

This is what it is
to die.

My heart beats faster,
her estuaries within;
The light of her lie
Beckoning me.

The Plough

Lizzy Harrison

My name in the sky was The Plough, though my child called me a saucepan, one of her human cooking utensils. She had seen me one day, pointing at me, shouting my name to her parents like she had made a brilliant discovery. Days after days she continued to look at me, the saucepan in the sky.

It wasn't until after her birthday when she finally called me by my real name.

It was dark, back then, when she rolled up her blind, gazing at the sky when she was supposed to be sleeping. 'You do look a bit like a Plough, don't you? You're always there for me, always watching me. Like a guardian angel, and I never fail to find you,' she whispered into the night.

It was rare to be spoken to, addressed directly by humans. This small girl, longing for something I couldn't quite place, called out for me. The soft emotion in her whisper was innocent and pleading. I tried my best to respond, to brighten myself. To remind her I was here; I could hear her.

When she laid her eyes on my constellation again, looking up after years of forgetting, the familiarity of my shape gave her comfort wherever she went. When the light of the sun dimmed, she would cast her eyes upwards, magnetically pulled to the lights in the sky.

She shared her secrets with me, with all of us, showed us her pain and basked in our silence as we helped her to reach a moment of peace. She was obsessed and somehow still maintained her child-hood ignorance, believing in the magic of starlight. She called us science as she had been taught, but her imagination always prevailed. That much was evident in the way she spoke about us with intimacy, like she already knew that we were so much more than atoms and energy. To her I was something meaningful, her heartbeat was engraved into me.

I am here, I can hear you.

Some days she would cry, overwhelmed by looking at us. Other times her stare would remain blank and distant, her thoughts and mind lost to me. I wanted to reach out and share my warmth each time she fought the cold to see me.

I am here, I can hear you.

I was warned by Orion that my attachment to this human, this child I loved, was growing too strong. If I continued down this path I may fall from the sky, and she would never see me again. Artemis of the moon warned me of the heartbreak to follow if it did occur. Apollo of the sun warned me that humans saw us as temporary, that she only saw me in the darkness, when it helped her most.

Liar, liar, liar!

I did not believe him, for he did not know her as well as I did.
   But…I kept my distance all the same.
   She was my favourite part of stardust; I couldn't lose her. Though the distance between us hurt, she began to smile more.

I will protect you.

It surprised me most when she shrunk away from the new life she was living. She had travelled far and whenever she was accompanied by someone else, she would stop and look up again, reminding them to open their eyes.

I will keep your secrets.

I wished she would share her thoughts – the spiralling thoughts and feelings which she showed me – to someone who could hold her, love her as dearly as she deserved to be loved. She craved the physical comfort that I could not give, and I wept for her.

I am sorry, sorry, sorry.

She loved me so much yet hated herself. If she only realised that we created her very being, made her who she was. That what she admired most about us was also in her. But she couldn't accept that. She continued watching, longing for something she could never receive – the comfort of the universe to dry her tears.

Child of stardust. Love yourself.
You are what is great in the universe.

As she continued to age, she stopped growing and spent more time with me. At night she sat, a steaming cup of human sustenance in her container, and whispered up at me.

'One day I will join you up there. I'll escape this world and go to yours, so very far away from this one.'

I felt my energy quicken as her words struck me, her solemn whisper, a promise. She would join us most definitely, a child of the universe, lover of the stars. Of me.

'I always wondered what it was that made you special…but I figured it out.'

She smiled to me, wiping tears from her eyes as she sat in the silence, almost as if she knew I was answering.

You are special.

'You're special, because to me, you remind me of home. Not the place, but the feeling of it.'

You are my comfort.

'With you I am never truly lost.'

I love you; I love you; I love you.

With this declaration, I faded quicker than ever, fearing the fall. If I disappeared for eternity, I would break her heart. She searched for me but could never find me. I wanted to call out to her but could only cry from space.

Artemis, in her bright glory, granted me comfort and consoled my tears with another promise. She promised that when the moon was full, she would listen to the star child as I had. She would take my place until we could join each other again.

Now she was no longer a child, but a woman, yet still a child to the universe. Her features were fascinating, and her posture was elegant, like an angel sent from our creators, a perfect example of how the stardust created years ago could create greater things so far in the future.

'You showed me the stars, before you left,' she spoke.
    'You showed me comfort when I couldn't find it.'
    'Why are you hiding from me? I only wish to see you.'
    She played with her hair, chewed at her perfect nails, and scratched at her unmarked skin. Tears streamed down her face as she placed her head in her hands. Defeated and drained, she whispered one last plea:
    'I need you.'
    Artemis prevented me from healing your aching heart, Apollo dimmed my light. Only Orion aided you and you followed him to me, where I was forced to hide in your night sky.
    Behind clouds, behind grey and black, you followed Orion's arrow and saw my dim shine. A mirror of your own tears, as I cried with you.
    You whispered, a dark and frightening tone in your voice as you disappeared inside your home.

'We are ashes and stardust.'

The next morning you disappeared from the Earth. Your soul slipped away.

But you flew towards me.

I love you; I love you; I love you!

For the first time, you responded, the twinkle of your soul as bright as the pole star. Tears of joy pooled in your eyes as you whispered.

'I always keep a promise.'

The Ninth Step

Hannah Harvey

I stand at the top of these steps.
Nine in total.
Dark and unknown, a journey I must take.
I cannot go up, so I tiptoe down

to the eighth step.
I hear the wind howl.
Thunder roars in anguish and rain crashes
    against a once shiny window.
I cower, and run down

onto the seventh step.
The gentle pattering of drizzle.
A soft sadness spread across my heart.
I pause, reflect this choice of journey,
gently step down

onto the sixth step.
The sky a misty grey. A world so accepted.
Yet so strange.
I wipe away a tear, then jump

onto the fifth step.
I ran up this one, breathless and sweaty –
It now stands waiting with a strange echo.
As I step down again,
I question my chosen life, wonder at my fears,
fall

onto the fourth step.
Pick myself up,
and look out as the clouds melt away, grey to blue.
Almost smile, leap

onto the third step.
Shake off my rain splattered jacket.
Beautiful colours faint in the sky. Gently step down

onto the second step.
Gazing out – a patchwork of creamy blue sky, in contemplation.
Birdsong flows.
A need to trust before I run down

onto the first step.
Puddles soaked up by a tentative sun.
One final look –
tread from cracked wood and cold tears
to peaceful steps along a thick carpeted floor.

Taboo

Anna Jackson

They told us that it's a dirty word
Vagina
Their lips curled around it like
They were spitting venom.
Call it something else
They say,
Foo foo, *privates*, *pussy*,
But that won't stand up in court.

Shut up, be quiet,
Don't you dare interrupt,
Gosh she raised her voice,
Must be that time of the month.
Cover up,
Show more skin,
Don't be a fucking prude.
Sit down, look pretty,
Smile for us bitch,
Don't you know how
To take a fucking compliment?

I'm sick and I'm tired
Of playing these games,
We teach women that they
Need a man to know their worth.
That their virginity is sacred,
Like a dick has the power
To change who you are.
Grow a pair of balls?
I say grow a pair of tits
If you really want a challenge.

Clapham

Karen MacKenzie

I came late to gin,
by way of whiskey and pills.
But it was pints back then
that filled the cracks
every time someone cut
the thread I was hanging on by.

Now, it's like she never existed,
her face redacted before the internet
could claim to know her. But
there are photographs, a bit dog-eared,
threadbare, a little like this memory…

A bar, noisy, laughter
friends of friends,
then a gap…before
it picks up again in the dark;
more laughter, turning
naturally to that warmth.

Just that one visit to Clapham.

Imperfect Timing

Fritha Macleod

The light speaks for you that you are here,
when I am finally ready to close my eyes,
why this time you choose to appear?

I send out words when you disappear.
Your signals break through the disguise,
the light speaks for you that you are here.

When my feelings sour too severe,
and sharing the night is a risk unwise,
why this time you choose to appear?

Stale silence, the worst to hear.
I am grateful you bring a warm reprise,
the light speaks for you that you are here.

Quiet thoughts shaken by a rising cheer,
your happy voice a sharp surprise.
Why this time you choose to appear?

Our conversations break and persevere,
against the empty hours that arise.
The light speaks for you that you are here.
Why this time you choose to appear?

all by myself

Sophie Marlowe

distance is moving to the other side
of the world at the age of five

   — i was nearly six

distance is having to make new friends and learn
about this new land but that's easier at nearly six

distance and i had grown close and comfortable
but i was only a kid so i was oblivious

to the distance between my mum and
my dad and the distance between my dad
and my brother

but i discovered a new brand of
distance at the tender age of seven

   — eight next month

when the ground beneath shook and
the cliffs roared and the dust blanketed
us all in this small seaside valleys

and i was by myself.

i didn't know where my parents were
and i didn't know where my brother was
until he found me

and my newly discovered and hated
brand of distance was put into play by
mother nature once again

  — i was eight

the ground shook and the cliffs roared and
the dust blanketed us in that small seaside valley and i was once again

all by myself.

Shatter

Amy Power

Promise me

you will not break yourself
in half

to make someone else
feel whole.

there's a metaphor about
setting yourself on fire
to keep another warm.

but fire
warms those in its proximity.

fire doesn't shrink itself –
fire rises and
welcomes you into its
embrace.
Fire spreads and
e x p a n d s .

it does not break.
it does not shatter.

Dreamscape

Elisabeth Pratt

Dreaming.

That's what life had become.

She was unsure if she was ever going to wake up. The dreams had been going on for so long that she had begun to doubt her own reality. Fear had set in a while ago, and now all that remained was the slow, maddening, downward spiral to terror. Nothing was real to her anymore, yet her fears still felt so permanent.

She had been running from something for so long...or had it been running to? Her mind had warped all memories, there was nothing left but her instincts, and even those could not be trusted anymore.

Existence had become nothing to her.

She wished for death but had no idea how to die.

She could have been dead all this time and not remembered.

She couldn't summon the courage to remember much anymore, never mind her life on the outside, or even if she had one.

Did she have parents? What were their names? What did they do? Were they divorced? Together? Did she have any siblings? How many? What were their names? Were they dead too? Were they happy?

It was easier to forget.

The questions had been spinning through her head for such a long time now, so long she couldn't even recall when the questions had begun and or if they had ended. It had become one giant loop of broken memories and fright followed only by forgetting and being brutally reminded once more.

She longed for anything other than loneliness.

Scenes blurred around her on occasion, rooms and words that would have meant something to her if she could only understand. They still managed to frighten her though, each one embodying enough of an eerie alarm that even the most shattered of minds could discern.

Always followed by a vision, the only one she could remember so clearly, the colours radiant and sharp, the picture no longer a blurred mess, a memory she could not forget yet the one she wanted removed the most.

Bridge Span

Natalie Roe

Standing at the edge of the riverbank, the Humber Bridge looms above me. Its span is two kilometres wide, stretching north-to-south, linking two edges of the same estuary. Throughout my childhood, it was the longest single span bridge in the world. How impressed me and my schoolfriends were at this piece of trivia! I love this view from the Hessle Foreshore, looking at the bridge reaching across, hearing both the roar of the traffic above but also the lapping of the water on the shingle. Ancient and modern. The two towers always seemed to be letter H's to me:

H for Humber. H for Hull.

The sun has already set, creating last gasps of light across the silver sky. The reflection from the lampposts on the bridge ripple through the dark water, breaking up the image, like they're the submerged lights of antique, ghostly vessels. The River Humber – or Humbri as it was known in Roman times – means 'dark river' or 'river covered in darkness'. I wonder if its characteristic mucky brown colour was apparent then as it is now. Another translation is 'covered in shadows.' I like the idea of the passing Romans travelling from Lincoln to Brough, naming the river after its dark colouring, or seeing the shadows play in the water, like I can see now.

My family have lived along the Humber for generations, from the tip of Spurn Head on the East coast, far west into the Yorkshire countryside; in Skeffling, Paull, Hull, all along the river right up into its tributaries and canals, to where my great-great-great-grandmother lived, in Thorne. They all had jobs linked to the Humber in some way. One was the Paull lighthouse keeper, one the vicar of the Holderness coastal parish, another a trawler captain.

Many were lightermen, skippers of the lighter ships or barges along the river, travelling the inland waterways, carrying cargo. Coal, grain, linseed oil; they moved goods from the up-water factories to the docks to ship them for trade at home and abroad; navigating through the water either by steam, tide, or by their own muscle. It wasn't bridged in their day. Any journey from one side to another was on land, passing the long way sixty miles around via Goole. Perhaps by taking the ferry from the Hull-side Victoria Pier to New Holland in Lincolnshire, or in older times, via the aptly named North and South Ferriby.

My gran used to tell me, when she was a girl in the 1920s, there would be so many boats in the Humber that children used to leap over from one to another. Hopscotching across, you could reach almost the middle of the river – half a mile's distance. Now, a hundred years later, it's empty. I see no boats at all. Of course, she would have also seen the ferry journeying across its daily timetable. She even saw the Zeppelin crash into the Humber in 1921. Now there are vapour trails from aeroplanes high up and the only river-traffic are the vehicles on the bridge.

From here I'm struck by the vastness of the open space, not just the width of the estuary, measured by the span of the bridge, but also the length of the river. To my right, it snakes off into the distance. Its convergence splits into two upstream tributaries, the Ouse and the Trent. On my other side, the river curves, the shoreline spreads out like two arms trying to embrace. In this dusky hour, the lines of the riverbanks are quite visible on both sides. The glittery lights of the docks illuminating and tracing the shape of the shore, out to the North Sea. Disappearing out into the ever-darkening distance, you could imagine the two sides meet in the middle somewhere. Instead, they both course away from each other, curving around to make the dog's tail of Spurn Head on the north bank; bending into the coastline of North-East Lincolnshire on the south side. The water is constantly moving today, choppy, rippling and glinting with the tide. The bridge is tall and steely in the twilight, illuminated by fairy-light threads along the cables.

I don't work on the Humber – who does anymore? I work inland, far away from the water. I stand on the shore and feel the disconnect. My world is in an office; a desk and a chair, neon strip lights, driving to work in a car. For them, it was the beams of the lighthouse, the shadows on the water, travelling on foot or by oar. I have a life they wouldn't recognise. I feel emotionally landlocked; a disconnect from previous generations, the tide rolling away from me.

Standing at the river, I smell seaweed in the air. The chill of the evening catches in my throat as I breathe, inhaling the cold and feeling it in my chest. The wind whips around my cheekbones, causing them to ache. Under my feet are the crunchy pebbles and washed-up driftwood. I imagine they're broken bits of fence posts, and broken stones, cut up by the river. It's the water-pressure changing the shape of the land around it. Across the span of the estuary, I see the distance of time, as well as space. Looking to the past is fragmented, like looking through rippling dark water. The connection feels intangible to me these days, but standing here at the banks of the Humber, I feel the tide pull me to the past.

Yem

Elliott Scriven

Up here we've seen it all
we've kicked and we've fought
with our backs to the wall, for too long
we have been a city, forgotten.

The shadows of yesteryear still loom large,
where the blue bastard bullies,
spat in the faces of our ancestors,
and damned us with
recession,
repression,
depression.

And yet, that's why I love where I'm from,
I love that we embrace our past;
I love that we are a city reborn
from the ashes of those who worked

In the dark
In the smoke
In the heat
In the dirt.

Our community is its heartbeat,
no matter how far I go,
or what becomes of me
I am still a 'wee bonny lad',
bleeding black and white,
with Geordie bones crafted
from strongest shipyard steel.

I never forget where I come from,
Nor, the strength it took to leave.
My heart will forever belong
to yem.

A Metaphoric Life

Jayne Stead

The shimmer of the Spanish sun casts my small, seven-year-old shadow across the bright blue bucket wedged in the sand. An awning of sorts. Crouching on my haunches, knees nearly at my ears, I peer into the sea scooped world that has become a rock pool in miniature. Sand carpets the bottom, water up to the ridge, threatening to overflow. My brother has just captured a crab and dropped it with a splash into this doll's house version of the ocean.

He is off back to the brimming rocks in the distance looking for more treasure. His store-bought fishing net over his brown shoulder, like a holidaying Dick Whittington. I am the homemaker. Stirring the sand until it resembles the seabed, I arrange the rocks and tuck the seaweed in a pretty fish tank formation. I am unafraid of the crab as it has hunkered deeply into its spiral shell. Anyway, it is tiny, and I am curious; big and strong. I drop in a final white pebble and some empty shells saved in my pocket and the stage is set. I tip myself onto my knees and peer over the bucket, my long, salty, red hair creating a sheer curtain framing the rim.

Nothing happens for a while. I can feel the sun burning my exposed neck, but I am seven and do not think of the pink damage it will do. I am superbly still. My eyes never leave the shell that will become a crab again. I am finally rewarded by a tiny, hairy red leg and a wisp of an antenna creeping from the safety of the shell to feel the water for vibrations. I have seen pictures of Hermit crabs in my Ladybird *Book of the Sea*, and, with a thrill, I realise this is one. I wait patiently for the other red legs, and eyes on stalks, to appear. The crab unfurls like a magician's hand – one finger at a time. It sways slightly in the water finding its way. It's pincered front legs embed in the sand and suddenly the shell is alive and moving. Hoisted up, it forms a peculiar back-pack that seems of the crab, yet not. It is clear it feels confident in its new environment. I congratulate myself on creating a proper home from home that has convinced the crab it is back in the sea.

It starts to explore and leaves trails as it scutters across the bucket's sandy floor. The few inches gap must seem like a mile to such a tiny creature. It rolls itself over the white pebble, circles the seaweed and comes to rest at the small collection of perfect, empty molluscs I have spent the week collecting. It's feelers hover above the largest shell. A whelk-type structure ridged and grey-white. It is nearly twice the size of its current one. I can hardly believe such a small creature can pull something this large towards it in such an easy tug. Breathless, I realise what is about to happen.

I fling my hair up and look around me to share the anticipation. My parents are too far away. Laid on towels, their faces are up to the sun, eyes closed. My brother is still a huntsman dot in the distance. A cut of disappointment, that I have a treasure but no one to share it with, is quickly replaced by the thrill of privilege. This show is just for me.

Returning to my own private performance, I shade the pail again and watch the tiny red crab. No bigger than a thumbnail, it pushes its own shell in a backwards motion away from itself. Weaving this way and that, it quickly and expertly uncoils itself. The wispy, striking front legs soon reveal a soft pink curl that looks vulnerable and like a sweet. Two halves that don't match. In a trice it swings its body round, covering the space in seconds and places itself in its new home. To all the world it looks like it has been there all along. It retreats fully for good measure, resurfaces to shed some sand debris, and finally settles on the mock seabed looking very pleased with itself.

I am seven and do not know how this memory will return to me again and again over the years. Every time I move house. Renting. When I finally buy my first home. Even when, as a young woman, I feel the relief of getting through my own front door after returning late from a night out. That feeling of tucking in tightly. Safe passage. The human need for shelter and refuge writ large in a blue bucket on a Benidorm beach.

But never do I feel it more than when I arrive at university. I am given a single room on the top floor of the tallest block that the college has to offer. The distance between my door and my neighbours is close yet it seems like miles. To fit in, to make new friends, we can be found leaning on these door jambs, rooms open behind us, chatting grades, backgrounds, places of origin. All of us so far from our first home. Our best faces forward. Our backs to our newly chosen bigger shell. For now. Tentatively exploring, antennae waving. Hoping the world will be big enough to have us when our time comes.

Chasing Ghosts

Hazel Storm

The deft form of a pale stag unfurled through the undergrowth. Low sounds of rustling and bellows of exhaling breaths filled the night chorus. Tales of a white beast had long since haunted the moorlands. Such folklore entranced even the hardiest of wind-beaten men. There was a longing, a pining to believe in something – anything more than barren mundanity.

With a coaxing breath of wind great horns of bone lifted in alarm. Eyes scanned the treeline. Pale hues lingered a moment. Backing off a step the beast turned aside, bolting into the undergrowth. A movement so quick and fleeting that it would nourish tales of the moor ghost for the generations to come.

He had never believed in it. James never believed in much of anything. What was one more ghost lost to the heather lands when a thousand more bucks stood boldly and awaited the cull? Sarah believed. Sarah had always believed. Her hands clasped around a flask, eyes wild with life, recanting the tale in as many incantations as she could muster. The thought left him cold. A long way away now from her, from the warmth of flasks. The warmth of her.

The gun was cold and heavy in his hand. That was real.

On the cusp of the moor a copse of trees stood sentry. The air was brisk. A brooding fog had settled in, digging its reach between the birches, holding them tightly in its grasp. The ground crunched beneath his boots. His breath hung in the air. The heat clung to him, as did the mist.

The trail of bodies dented the ferns. The path of a diligent herd. Walking the same paths. The same tracks. Again, and again.

Hoisting the strap over his shoulder, James followed on obediently. As the ferns gave way, the ground inclined rapidly. Slipping and stumbling to stay level he gritted his teeth, sank his hands into the mud and crawled. He pressed low to his stomach at the peak and slid the strap from his shoulder. The moor laid bare – stripped of trees and safety. The click of the gun's chamber pierced the air. James exhaled deeply, settled his mind, and waited.

The mist came and went, rolling in and out of the hills. It had stilled now, resting close to the ground, calm and at peace as if at the end of a pilgrimage. A low bellow roused James from his trance. A shadow peeled from the foggy void. Dark at first, obscured. It paused, waiting behind the veil. Marked boldly by the backlight, the lean of its muscle rippled in a slow shiver. With his brow pressed to the scope James pulled the trigger. The bellow came again. James jarred his head from the gun waiting for the fall of the stag. It stumbled, staggered a moment, then disappeared. He cursed beneath his breath.

Grabbing his gun, James slid down the embankment. The mist clung to him. It cloaked everything in its path. He hadn't missed. Blood speckled in the grass marked his target. In the distance a low bellow called out to the air. The strap returned to his shoulder. With his head firmly down, he began to trek.

The tracks were few and far between, growing shorter in distance with every step. His feet ached. A more empathetic man may have wondered how the beast could still be going, stumbling on. Daylight was fading fast. The ground was hardening with the freezing air.

Leaning against a rock jutting out from the earth, a broken mantle. James took a knee, turning it this way and that. Gnarled passageways splintered through the antler. The trail he had been following was nowhere to be seen. The mist had closed in once more around him. The stag was enclosed into the labyrinth, the minotaur yet to be found. The prongs of the antler reached out like fingers, pointing the way. Closer now, the bellow called forth again.

James walked on – the mist so dense and suffocating now that he walked blindly. The sharp crackle of undergrowth halted him. There, the deep shadow of it stood. De-crowned. A mere few steps away. He settled his fingers on the strap. Paused a moment. And then a moment again. The breaths of the stag clouded rapidly, forcing its way in short bursts of steam through the fog. He did not bolt this time, merely swung his head low and turned to walk on once again, vanishing behind the veil.

For a while James did not follow. It no longer felt like his path to walk. He was no more than a spectator, following on obediently to bear witness. He thought briefly of her – Sarah. The way she'd turn away, flinching, before the trigger was pulled. James longed to confess his will to let just this one go. Just this one. But the empty air beside him was barren and bare. And duty still lay ahead.

The light was in its final standing. James clung to his coat. The wind blew in great gusts, sweeping away the haze. The heather faded almost to black in the low light. He was unsure how far he had walked. He followed only, blindly, the stumbling tracks through the vast growth. The land had flattened out. Deep gullies cut into the earth. The shrubbery gave way to grass. Then sharply to tarmac. The road sliced through the moor in a rigid long straight. James dropped the strap from his shoulder.

In the middle of the road, the white stag lay still.

James hung the strap from his arm, his shoulders sagging low. He looked down in silence. The wind whimpered softly and stilled at his feet as the last of the light surrendered to the horizon.

Baby

Jack Taggart

She couldn't remember from whom she bought the house, or anything about the previous owners in fact. She was just happy to have a place called home. The house itself was situated at the end of a long, endless row of bland and repetitive terraced houses. She loved the location of home, upon a steep hill, away from the noise and unrestrained pursuits of those in the bustling streets around her.

She lay one night, in her perfect home, only to be awoken by the most horrific, stomach-turning screaming coming from somewhere inside the house. She shot up, forgetting where she was for a moment before gathering her breath. She closed her eyes, inhaling through her nose before releasing it composedly throughout her mouth. She got out of bed and turned to her husband.

'She's up.'

Her husband didn't move. It was her turn with baby, just as it was every other night. Why should this one be any different? She creeped to the door of the bedroom silently, trying to not wake up her resting husband. She twisted the knob of the door which squeaked ever so softly. She turned back, hoping to not see him awoken. He remained still, unmoved by her actions.

As she entered the nursery, the heinous crying grew louder, as if it was driven from her own thoughts and memories. She pressed the switch upon the once-pink wall of the nursery and on came the night lights. The endless possibilities of the moon and stars lit up the ceiling, highlighting a damp, green stain that blended with the shadows of space. An unnatural coloured liquid dripped to the floor, creating a puddle which grew larger by the day, generating a putrid smell that she had learned to ignore. She walked through the puddle with bare feet, as if it wasn't even there, moving closer to the cot which sat in the middle of the room.

She moved in and twisted the cot around to face her. What was once a white, luxurious bed for baby had gone green with mould, rotting, and festering as time passed. She rocked the cot, smiling at baby. Her smile was her own truth. She was happy. The horrific screaming did not stop as she began to sing.

'Hush, little baby don't say a word. Papa's gonna buy you a mocking bird.'

Her once large and happy smile began to shrink as baby's cries grew louder, filling her ears and mind with the agonising scream until she could no longer hear herself think. She ran back to the bedroom, knowing that baby needed her father tonight.

He didn't wake. She stared at him. His eyes open, gazing at the ceiling just as he was before she left to see to baby. She began to get frustrated as he ignored her. Anger spread from her chest into her face, turning it a blood red. She was sick of him always lying there.

'Lazy. You do nothing around this house. You're lucky I'm on top of things or I'd be sending you packing.'

Just as she had finished ranting, she noticed the blaring sound of silence echoing through the walls of home. She turned back to him, who still laid motionless, and smiled. She skipped away with a spring in her step back to the nursery, standing once again in the puddle as she walked to the cot. She looked inside at baby, who lay silent in the decaying pit.

'Would you like to sleep with Mummy and Daddy tonight?'

Baby didn't respond, nor make any movement. A tear ran down her face, past her nose and on to her lip where it sat for a moment before falling into baby's cot, merging with the other liquid that had sprouted in there over time. She reached into the cot and pulled out the doll that lay. The hair had rotted from the porcelain scalp and only one of the two eyes remained lodged in its face. The rotting dampness that the doll had sat in dripped from its worn-out clothes, onto her feet and over the floor of the nursery as she carefully carried it from the cot to her bedroom.

'Looks like we have a little visitor tonight.'

The smile that shined across her face was that of a true mother. Her own nuclear family together as one. She cradled baby in her arms as her pyjamas began to stain from the moisture spreading from the doll's clothes. She looked at her husband who was nothing more than a portrait. She stroked the face that sat upon the broken canvas and closed her eyes tightly, hoping it would be morning soon. She was happy. Baby was at rest.

Amber Alert

Cheyenne Uustal

Tick. Tick. Tick.

I have lost more than just you. I have lost my ability to be me. I have lost the life I knew and loved, and the future I had imagined for us.

For eight years, I tucked you into bed, dried your tears, bathed you, cared for you and hugged you. Being your mother is my greatest accomplishment and favourite identity. Now I'm scared I'll never hear you call me mum again.

I wish I had hugged you tighter and longer when I had the chance.

Instead, I'm sat at the window watching parents rush their children to school like ants scuttling towards a picnic. They have no idea what we're going through and yet I still wonder how they can live their lives like nothing has happened. The silence is deafening, breathing is painful, and sleeping is out of the question. I can't waste all that time doing nothing while knowing you might be out there scared and hurt. I can't even close my eyes without seeing your face – the same face that's plastered all over the news…

I leave the house with unwashed hair and bags under my eyes. I'm cuddling your favourite teddy – the pink fairy that you loved so much – and whispering words of encouragement to myself.

'Being at home is worse,' I tell myself. 'She'll be okay. You can do this.'

A photograph of you lays crumpled in my pocket so I can ask any passer-by if they've seen you. Some of them don't even look at it before they shake their heads and walk away. Would it be the same if it was their child? The rest of them just give me a pitiful look that I've grown to hate. Every no squeezes my heart tighter than the last.

Tick. Tick. Tick.

I'm with a search party looking for you. They've got us walking in a line and have split us up into five groups to cover as much ground as possible. They show me a map littered with red *x*'s marking where we've already looked and black circles for where we're searching today. We walk for miles. Not one strand of grass is left untrodden. I feel bad for admitting that, even if it wasn't good news, I was excited to see your face again. It's too dark to look now and yet another search party has ended without a satisfactory answer.

On my walk home I'm looking at the moon and I'm wondering if you are too. I hope it brings you comfort. I hope it reminds you that you're loved. I hope it reassures you that we're looking for you.

Where are you? You could still be on our street, or miles away on the other side of the country. It makes me feel sick just thinking about it. You belong at home with us. You belong in my arms.

Tick. Tick. Tick.

The police have asked me to do another public appeal.

'Please. I just want my little girl back,' I beg through my sobs. 'Someone somewhere must know something! Please come forward with any information you have even if you think it's insignificant! I just want her home safe!'

I break down in tears, so the senior detective takes over for me. He explains what we already know, which isn't much, if anything at all, and tells the public what they can do, which isn't much, if anything at all. I sit staring at a multitude of microphones, video cameras and flashes… I should be out there looking for you.

You've been missing for two days. I keep staring at the door waiting for you to come home, expecting to see your face like I have hundreds of times before. I wouldn't take it for granted this time. Not like I use to. Not like the mums in the streets, kissing their child's head and waving goodbye, not questioning whether they'll see them at the dinner table.

'You know what they say, a watched pot never boils,' your father mumbles into my hair. Is that supposed to be funny? I know he's only trying to lighten the situation, but it seems a little inappropriate, don't you think? You're missing! It's not the time for jokes! Still, his words repeat themselves over and over in my head and I pry myself away from the door. I'm willing to try anything at this point, but there's nowhere in the house that I don't feel your presence.

I can't even look out the window because it's raining. The thought of you out there in the cold and wet is unbearable.

The sound of the phone draws me from my thoughts. I don't think it even makes it to the second ring before I answer it. It's not your voice though. It's a deep, dry voice that sounds like sandpaper. In a thick Scottish accent, he tells me that they have a new lead and they're investigating a potential eyewitness.

Tick. Tick. Tick.

Time is running out. They say that the first seventy-two hours in a missing person case are the most vital. I know that, in reality, every hour matters. I know that with each tick of the clock it's another second that you are not home. Are you ever coming home? Are you safe? Are you hurt? Are you still alive? My mind is running wild with all the scenarios I picture you in. I need an answer.

This is the longest that we've ever been apart. What monster can separate a mother and their child?

170,000 people are reported as missing every year. More than half of those are children, and now you're one of them. When did you become a statistic? I wonder what statistic I'm going to be a part of.

While sat on your bed I'm looking at the moon and wondering if you are too, so that a piece of me is with you. I hope that soon you'll be back in my arms where you belong.

The York Centre for Writing

Schools Creative Writing and Literature Competition, 2022

The York Centre for Writing hosts an annual school's writing prize, inviting submissions of original prose, poetry or dramatic monologue. This year the theme for entries was the environment and the submissions reflect fascinating and imaginative takes on that theme. The school's prize is about encouraging and celebrating new writing. The entries we receive represent a generation of new talent and we wish we could publish all of the entries in this collection. What is clear from the following shortlisted entrants is that the future of writing is safe in their hands.

On the First Day I was Just a Boy

Ezra Spencer
(Huddersfield New College, Year 12)

On the first day I was just a boy.

Weak, whimpering – a wuss. Sat atop the splinter pocked board that I'd managed to salvage in the wreckage. Grasping hard on the wood my knuckles blanched and my innards twisted as I was outwardly paralysed in the blue abyss alone. Dumbly I hiccupped, snot dripping from my nose and leaking, disgustingly, like a puss gorged wound. My eyes were bloodshot and my cheeks would not dry.

About me the world rolled with apparent malice as the rocking motion had me sick to my stomach. Nausea bubbled up my noose tight throat, threatening to spew from wind chapped lips but I held tight, too rigid and afraid to ambush the ongoing battalions of waves. Curved and poised like scimitars on soldiers, advancing on the horizon. That was a thin black line, sturdy as the palm of Atlas, dividing two parallel planes of infinite blue.

Skating atop the surface my feet felt the crisp chill of the water as it lapped about my limp ankles. The cold felt like winter, frigid and hollowing, as it sapped the heat from my weary body. Pulling them out and into the hot glare of the sun I had only moments to relish the warmth that saturated my exposed flesh till I felt it burn. Trapped in this ill-tempered purgatory, neither comfortable in or out, I looked downwards for distraction.

It was little help, instead a growing sense of discontent filled my chest as I watched the parasites of the sea claim the carcass of my home. Nestled between heaped dunes of coral, sand and rock her ribs glittered beneath distorted sunbeams and I observed the many crustaceous ticks and scaled worms lurk through and about her ripped skin. They glutted themselves upon her innards and I at once resented them. But sick with the overpowering smell and taste of salt, there was little I could do aside from survive at the mercy of the abyss alone.

On the second day, I assume, I woke older.

Hunger was the first thing I felt as it gnawed at my innards and rebelled against my circumstances with deep guttural growls as though the minotaur traipsed my intestines like a labyrinth. Dejectedly my tongue butted against my pink gums and I tasted little more than salt and dirt.

Dirt.

The realisation dropped gradually as consciousness washed over me but suddenly I felt it tug and swallow and drown me whole, my body jolting upwards in response. Eyes splitting open, narrowing immediately out of fear of the harassment from the sun. For a moment the world was blinding white until it dimmed into something more palatable and I was greedily able to take in my surroundings. Looking to my feet first I saw and felt the baked sand beneath, it's heat embraced my skin and it's countless beads crept within the pockets of my skin, itchy but welcomed in the absence of bitter sea. Bubbling up and out the sound of my joy filled the quiet lull of the world, hooting and hollering over the ever present blue. I poured out the hot triumph from my lungs until each breath came heavy and my throat hoarse – there was victory in my soul.

Just as fast as the happiness had risen it was squashed soon after. Breathlessly I looked out again and stared at the endless blue. How gluttonous it was as it spread its girth across the sky and sea and melded into the horizon, all that I could see was blue spiked with white writhing like a snake but silent aside from the soft hiss of the waves. The motion of it, rocking back and forth, peaking and falling, rebelling and succumbing, sickened me.

And then I felt the rumbling beneath my feet, something deep and ancient muttering through my bones, my body a divining rod and my core a battery. Looking about I saw nothing aside from the sea and the sand which I then noted was decorated with stray shells, the odd bit of dried out and deadened coral that ominously lay shattered about the beach in a thin layer of funeral shroud. Following the sensation, I dug to find cool grey beneath the pale gold.

Was it stone? I first asked myself, muttering as my nails pressed up against the spongy substance.

Something shuddered and before I knew it the world had flipped. Rapidly the world spun, blue into white into gold into blinding yellow into deep blue again as I was tossed and subsequently doused into the frozen water. Submerged and afraid I kicked out, breathing ripping free of my chest and bubbling up for freedom above my head. The salt stung my eyes and for a moment in the blue I spied something black and glittering, alive amongst folds of grey wrinkles and hide.

Despite the menacing blue that gripped my clothes and pulled me down, my spasming limbs seemed to propel me up and free. Never have I ever breathed like that since, my windpipe having been whipped raw with each wracking breath. Collapsing onto the beach backed creature I cried.

On a day long after that I watched as a man.

We passed a city that day. In the darkness it glowed with vibrant lights like fallen stars. Observing it upon the back of the creature turned home, I could not help the sinking feeling within my gut. For so long I had floated by the infinite blue, skated atop drowned lands and forgotten ships, after a while none of it phased me but that day… Facing the possibility of civilization again?

Tendrils of dread rose up and drowned me.

There was no going back.

Framed Trees

Opal Stubbs
(Chesterfield College, Year 12)

I wish I were a tree,
Not just sometimes,
But most of the time,
Because,
While we sit inside, gathering dust,
They won't say we're beautiful,
They won't paint us. They won't paint me.
I myself an empty canvas,
I don't inspire.
And trees, they get painted,
Apple trees, orange trees, and cherry blossoms,
They all have a beauty,
That I cannot reach, that I cannot be.
Yet they age yearly,
Dying in winter,
Losing all its colour,
And still inspiration strikes,
Every crevice and flaw carved in the bark,
Is seen as perfect,
Paintings are made,
Trees become framed,
And I am left,

Deemed not worthy,
Sat upon the top shelf,
Neglected, and labelled ugly,
Alone.
Doing nothing,
Being nothing,
Disintegrating.
And becoming dust.

The Grass Above the Graves

Joshua Turton
(Notre Dame Catholic Sixth Form College, Year 13)

Back when nothing was to be done about
anything, the grass grew above the graves.
Yellow-green blades leaning into the wind
bending against pressure: the forces of
change that forged us. Veiling stone…quartz…marble…
Each bearing the Atlas' burden of a name.
Generations shrouded within a brief return
to true status quo.
The between of life and death
disintegrates – wind
rippling through the glorious, unkempt
boarder like a current; coursing presence
where its absence is on display.

Mesmerizing: that is all I can say
of the time the grass outgrew the graves and swayed.

Unzipped

Kizzy Wade
(Selby College, Year 13)

The following are instructions for the
  surgical unzipping of Kizzy Wade.
First draw a dot to dot on the patient's back,
  following the curves of the spine,
Each dot or dash connoting a milestone they had
  planned for, wished for, expected and the twists
their time will take,
Just ink blots to you but pearls of possibility to them,
  these will incised upon, cut, slashed,
The aftermath will not be neat, the skin will be fractured,
  a once linear journey adjourned either
side of gaping wounds,
I may add that there is a lot more to come
  before scarring even begins,
The hole, their future is now open to pure oxygen
  and improvement yes but also bacteria, germs,
disrupters,
You know you will soon fill it,
You lift the iron bar over them you let it hang in the air
  only for a second, knowing it will actually
stay there forever,
Finally it lays inside them cold like
  the doubt caused by this new reality,
It is abandoned the job that has been done, irreversible.

You turn your attention from the metal to marrow and bone,
You try to mould it into a more comfortable
    shape not just for them but for you. Success,
Now it's time to combine the two, take away
    some humanity to make space for steely perfect,
You don't believe in souls and nor do they but as
    you drill into the bone you're sure you drill into
theirs,
Any hope of being totally independent gone.
    Now bolted out of sight.
Just one more step before everything is correct,
    vertical without variation,
As you begin to put surgical needle to skin
    you begin feel something,
Sadness, anxiety, dread maybe hope,
You can't help but wonder if, as you bridge the gap
    from flesh to flesh you maybe creating a gap
between them and everyone else,
Because now they'll always be unusual, uncanny, unzipped

Acknowledgements

EDITORIAL AND PRODUCTION TEAM

Sam Whitwell (Team Leader), Evan Clay (Sub-team Leader),
George Barrett, Theresa Cameron, Jacob Currie,
Maisie Hallam, Elise Hesk, Amie Matthews,
Joshua Moran, Lewis Quinn, Amelia Rodgers.

BLOGS AND PODCASTS TEAM

Effie Warboys (Team Leader), Anna Jackson (Blogs Sub-team
Leader), Tarryn Watkins (Podcasts Sub-team Leader),
Iain Barclay, Josh Brittain, Thandie Grant, Katie Grimstead,
Sophie Marlowe, Kayleigh Paterson, Elliott Scriven.

MARKETING AND EVENTS TEAM

Kai Aspinall (Team Leader), Lilia Durrani, Georgina Klavins,
Ed Mate, Nathan Murphy, Bethany O'Flaherty,
Erica Prata, Becki Richardson.

OTHER MEMBERS OF THE BEYOND THE WALLS TEAM

Ethan Bould, Elle Brough.

Our thanks to Lendal Press and Valley Press
for their assistance with the anthology.